Table of Contents

How to Use This Book

This Premium Education Series workbook is designed to suit your teaching needs. Since every child learns at his or her own pace, this workbook can be used individually or as part of small group instruction. The activity pages can be used together with other educational materials and are easily applied to a variety of teaching approaches.

Contents
A detailed table of contents lists all the skills that are covered in the workbook.

Units
The workbook is divided into units of related skills. Numbered tabs allow you to quickly locate each unit. The skills within each unit are designed to be progressively more challenging.

Activity Pages
Each activity page is titled with the skill being practiced or reinforced. The activities and units in this workbook can be used in sequential order, or they can be used to accommodate and supplement any educational curriculum. In addition, the activity pages include simple instructions to encourage independent study, and they are printed in black and white so they can be easily reproduced. Plus, you can record the child's name and the date the activity was completed on each page to keep track of learning progress.

Teaching Tips
Some of the activity pages include teaching tips, which are designed to help you get the most out of the activity. They can also help you extend the learning experience beyond the workbook page.

Practice Tips
A comprehensive practice test helps prepare the child for standardized testing in a stress-free environment. Standardized testing can be a part of school curriculum as early as kindergarten, so it is important for a child to feel confident with the fill-in-the-circle testing format.

Answer Key
The pages in the back of the workbook provide answers for each activity page as well as the practice test. These answer pages allow you to quickly check the child's work and provide immediate feedback on how he or she is progressing.

Name_____ Date_____

Draw yourself.

My name is _____.

Teaching Tip: Talk about hair color and facial features and have the child draw his or her own picture. Write the child's name and have him or her use a finger to trace each letter. Then help the child read the sentence.

Name_____ Date_____

Color the cake. Add candles
to show how old you are.

I am _____ years old.

My birthday is on _____.

Teaching Tip: Talk about celebrating a birthday. Ask the child how old he or she is and have him or her color the cake and decorate it with the correct number of candles. Then write the child's age and birthday and help him or her read the sentences.

Name_____ Date_____

Draw your family.

There are _____ people in my family.

Teaching Tip: Talk about family members and have the child draw a picture of his or her family. Help the child count the people in his or her family. Then right the number and help the child read the sentence.

Name_____ Date_____

Color the pets that you like.

rabbit

dog

cat

fish

gerbil

bird

My favorite pet is _____.

Teaching Tip: Talk about different kinds of pets and have the child circle the pets that he or she likes. Ask the child what pet he or she likes the best. Write the name of the child's favorite pet and help him or her read the sentence.

Self-Awareness: Hands

Name_____ Date_____

Circle the children using their hands.

Teaching Tip: Talk about how the children at the top of the page are using their hands. Ask the child to tell you what the other children on the page are doing. Then have him or her circle the ones who are using their hands.

Name_____ Date_____

Circle the children using their feet.

Teaching Tip: Talk about how the child at the top of the page is using his feet. Ask the child to tell you what the other children on the page are doing. Then have him or her circle the ones who are using their feet.

The Senses: Seeing

Name_____ Date_____

Color 1 , 2 , 3 , and 4 .

Name_____ Date_____

Color what you can hear.

Name_____ Date_____

Circle what you can smell.

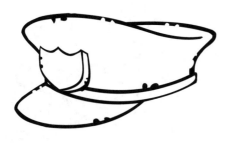 

Name_____ Date_____

Circle what you can touch.

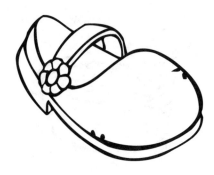

Name_____ Date_____

Color what you can taste.

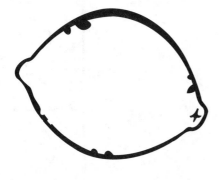

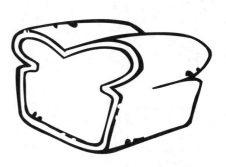

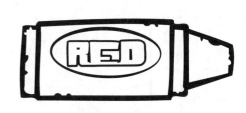

Name_____ Date_____

Draw a line to show what goes together.

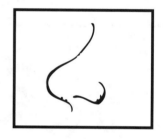

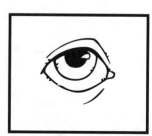

Name_____ Date_____

Circle the or .

Teaching Tip: Talk about the bear faces and how they show happy and sad feelings. Then have the child circle the face that shows how he or she would feel in each scene.

Name_____ Date_____

Circle the or .

Teaching Tip: Talk about the bear faces and how they show angry and surprised feelings. Then have the child circle the face that shows how he or she would feel in each scene.

Name_____ Date_____

Color the ones that are the same in each group.

Unit 2

Name_____ Date_____

Match the ones that are the same.

Name_____ Date_____

Match the ones that are the same.

Unit 2

Name_____ Date_____

Color the ones that are the same in each row.

Name_____ Date_____

Circle the one that is different in each group.

Unit 2

Name_____ Date_____

Color the one that is different in each row.

Name_____ Date_____

Color the one that is different in each row.

Name_____ Date_____

Color the one that is different in each row.

Classifying: What Belongs (I)

Name_____ Date_____

Circle what belongs in the .

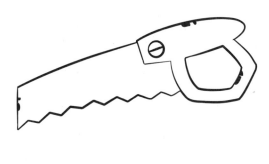

Name_____ Date_____

Color what belongs in the .

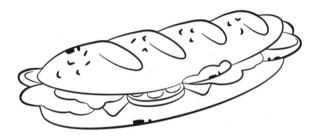

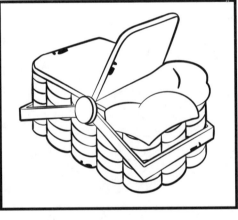

Name_____ Date_____

Draw an **X** on what does not belong.

Unit 2

Name_____ Date_____

Circle what does not belong in each row.

  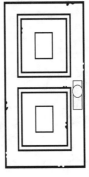 

Name_____ Date_____

Match the ones that go together.

Name_____ Date_____

Match the ones that go together.

Name_____ Date_____

Match the part to its whole.

Name_____ Date_____

Match the whole to its part.

Name_____ Date_____

Draw a line to what will happen next.

Predict: First and Next (II)

Name_____ Date_____

Circle what will happen next.

Name_____ Date_____

Draw lines to show the correct order.

1

2

3

Name_____ Date_____

Write **1**, **2**, and **3** to show the correct order.

☐   ☐   ☐

☐   ☐   ☐

Name_____ Date_____

Trace each line from **left** to **right**.

Unit 3

Name_____ Date_____

Trace each line from **left** to **right**.

Name_____ Date_____

Trace each line from **top** to **bottom**.

Unit 3

Name_____ Date_____

Trace each line from **top** to **bottom**.

Name_____ Date_____

Trace each line from **left** to **right**.

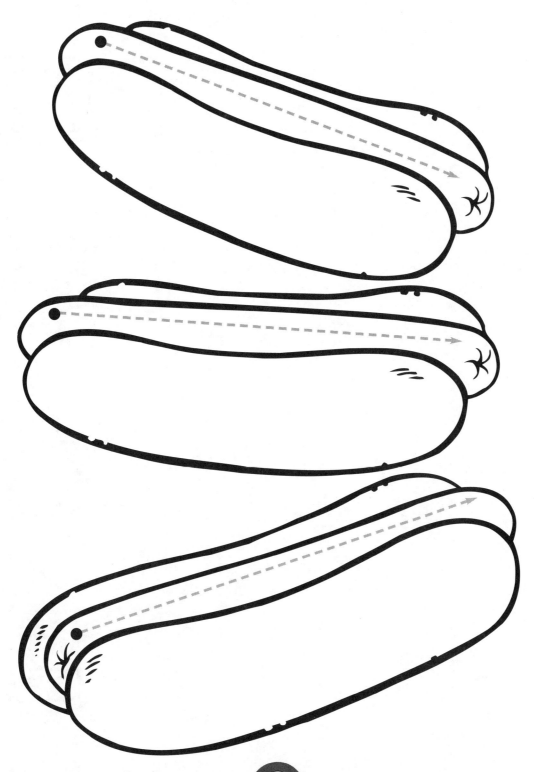

Unit 3

Trace: Zigzag Lines

Name_____ Date_____

Trace each line from **left** to **right**.

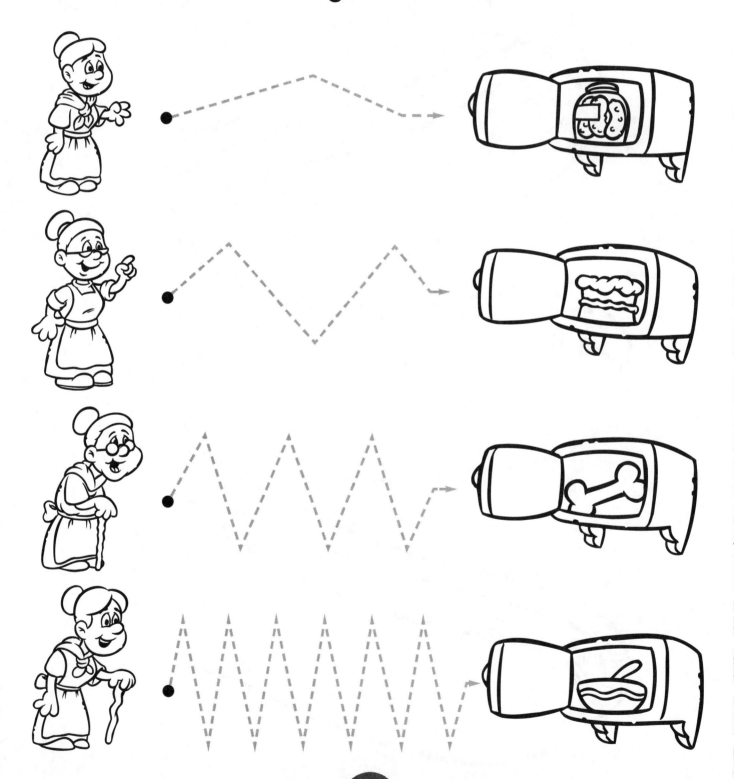

Name_____ Date_____

Trace each line from **left** to **right**.

Unit 3

Trace: Curvy Lines

Name_____ Date_____

Trace each line from **left** to **right**.

Name_____ Date_____

Trace the lines.

Unit 3

Name_____ Date_____

Trace the lines.

Name_____ Date_____

Trace the lines.

Unit 3

Name_____ Date_____

Draw the path to the gingerbread house.

Teaching Tip: Encourage the child to use his or her finger to find the way through the maze before drawing the path with a crayon.

Name_____ Date_____

Draw the path to Goldilocks.

Teaching Tip: Encourage the child to use his or her finger to find the way through the maze before drawing the path with a crayon.

Name_____ Date_____

Draw the path to the spoon.

Teaching Tip: Encourage the child to use his or her finger to find the way through the maze before drawing the path with a crayon.

Name_____ Date_____

Trace and write the letters.

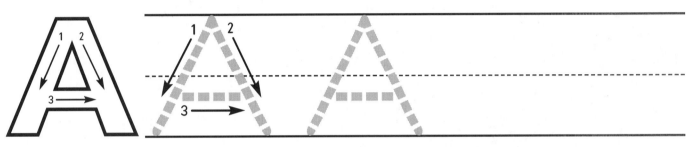

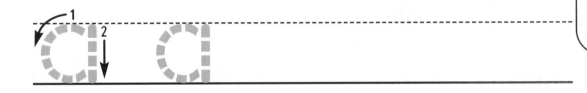

Circle each ant that has **A** or **a** on its hat.

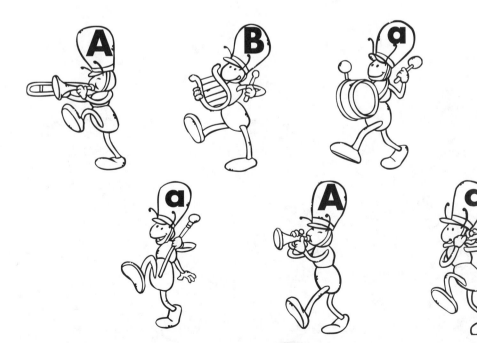

Name_____ Date_____

Trace and write the letters.

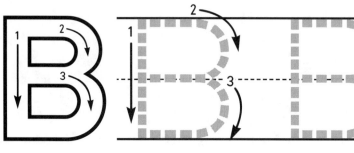

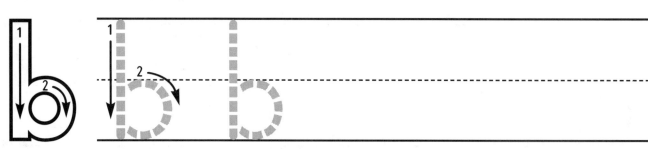

Color each balloon that has **B** and **b** together.

Letters: Cc

Name_____ Date_____

Trace and write the letters.

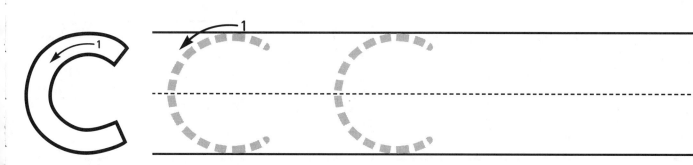

Circle each car that has **C** and **c** together.

Name_____ Date_____

Trace and write the letters.

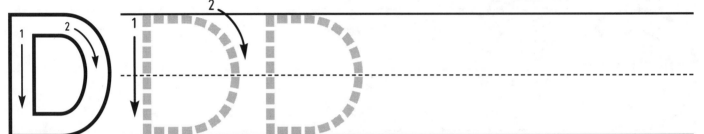

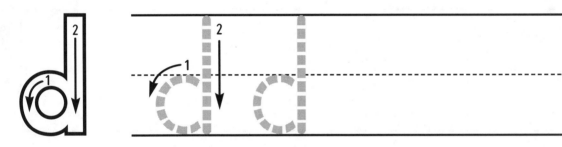

Find and circle each **D** and **d** in the picture.

Name_____   Date_____

Trace and write the letters.

Ee

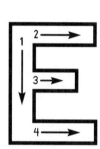

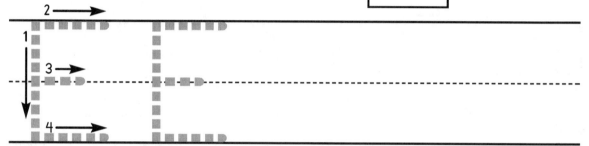

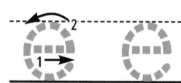

Draw a line from the **E** on the elephant to each **e** on a peanut.

Name_____ Date_____

Ff

Trace and write the letters.

F

f

Find **F** and **f** on the tic-tac-toe boards. Draw a line through three in a row to win each game.

F	A	B
F	C	E
F	D	A

f	f	f
e	b	d
c	a	b

c	b	a
e	d	e
f	f	f

F	D	E
C	F	A
B	D	F

Letters: Gg

Name_____ Date_____

Trace and write the letters.

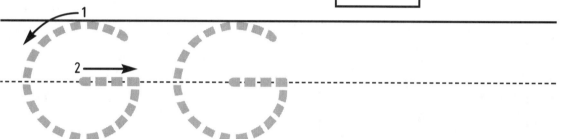

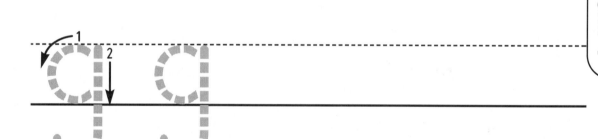

Color the spaces with **G** and **g** to see what the gorilla will play.

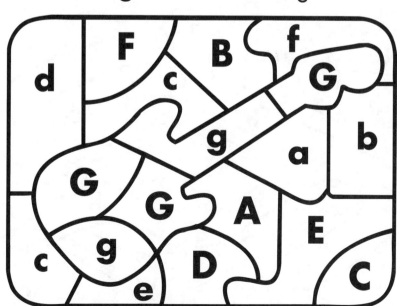

Name_____ Date_____

Trace and write the letters.

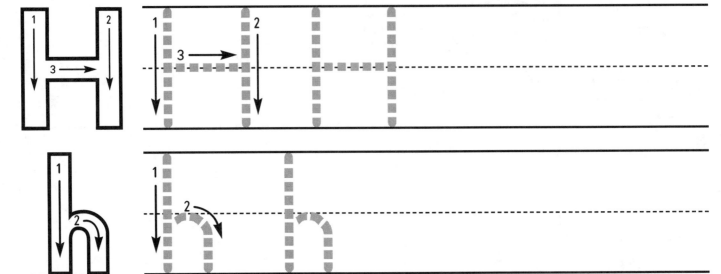

Follow the letters **H** and **h** to draw the path to the little hippo.

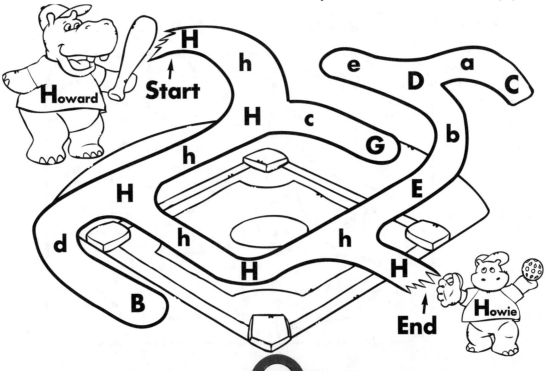

Name_____ Date_____

Trace and write the letters.

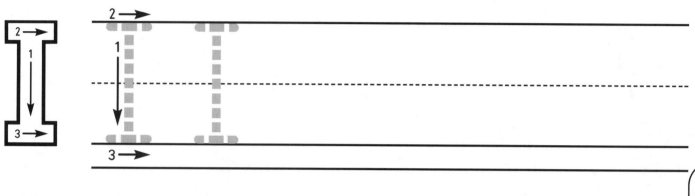

Color each ice cream scoop that has **I** or **i** on it.

Unit 4

Name_____   Date_____

Trace and write the letters.

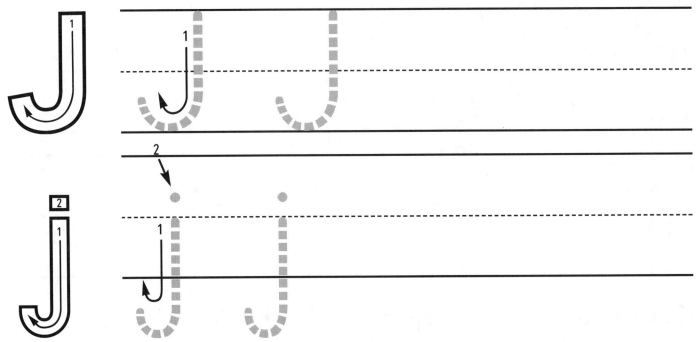

Draw a line from the juggler to each thing that has **J** or **j** on it.

Name_____ Date_____

Trace and write the letters.

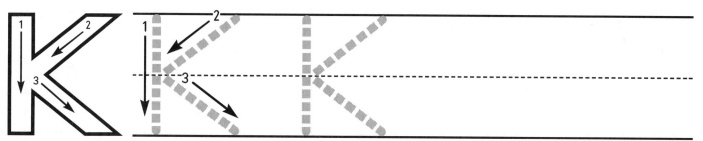

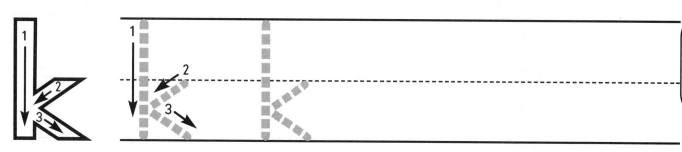

Unit 4

Draw a line from the kite to each **K** and **k** in the picture.

Name_____ Date_____

Trace and write the letters.

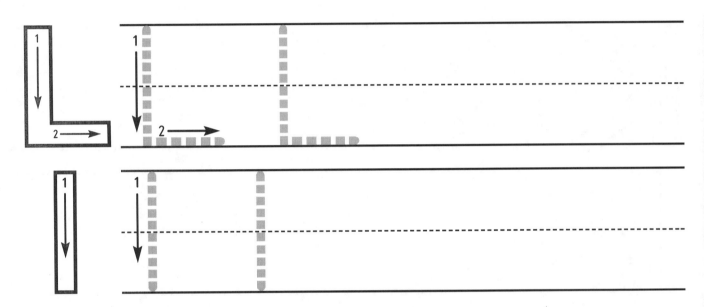

Cross out the letter on each log that is not **L** or **l**.

Name_____ Date_____

Write the missing letters.

Unit 4

Name_____ Date_____

Connect the dots from **a** to **l** to finish the picture.

e.

•d   •f   h•   •g

c.   •b

•i

•j

a.
↗
Start

l
↙
End

•k

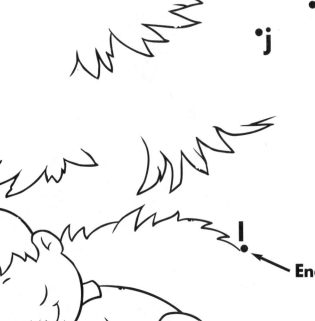

Name_____ Date_____

Trace and write the letters.

Mm

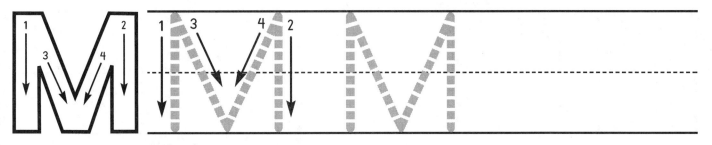

Follow the letters **M** and **m** to draw the path to the mittens.

Start

End

Name_____ Date_____

Trace and write the letters.

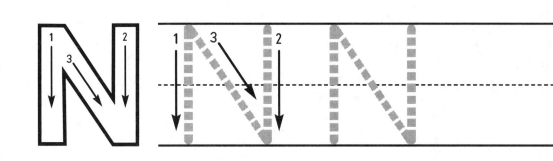

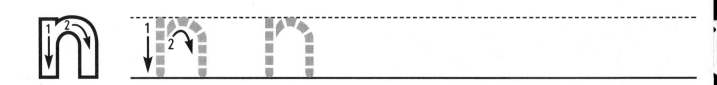

Color each nest that has **N** or **n** on it.

Name_____ Date_____

Trace and write the letters.

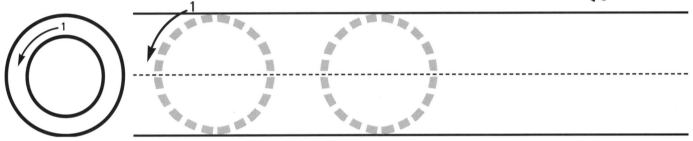

Color the spaces with **O** and **o** to see who is in the tree.

Name_____ Date_____

Trace and write the letters.

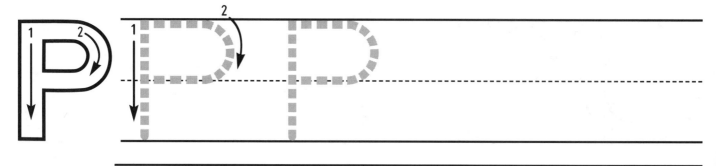

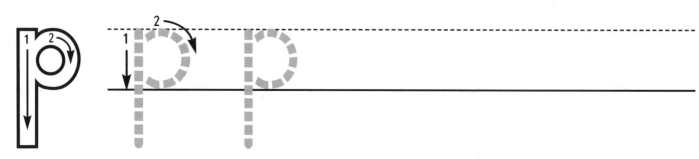

Circle each penguin that has **P** or **p** on it.

Name_____ Date_____

Trace and write the letters.

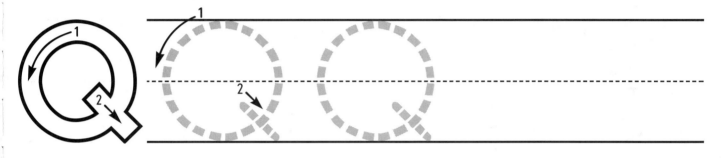

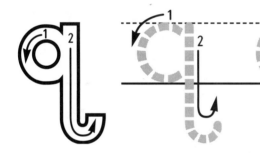

Color each shape on the quilt with **Q** or **q** in it.

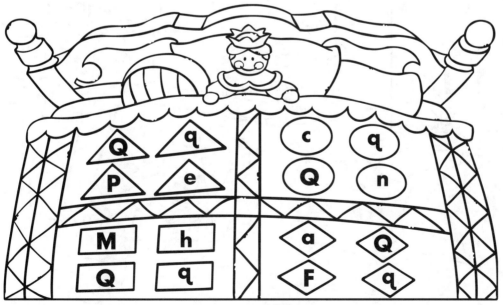

Name_____ Date_____

Trace and write the letters.

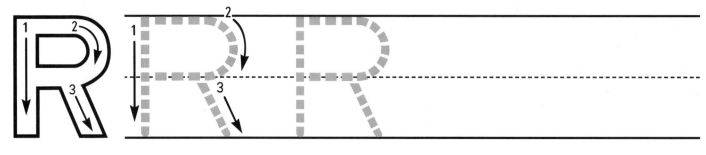

Color each robot that has **R** and **r** together.

Name_____ Date_____

Trace and write the letters.

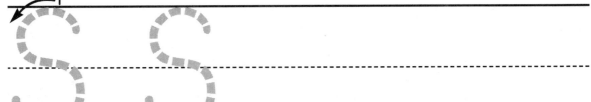

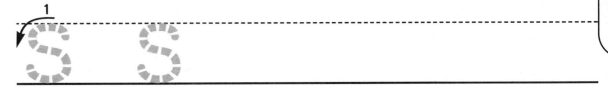

Find and circle each **S** and **s** in the picture.

Name_____ Date_____

Trace and write the letters.

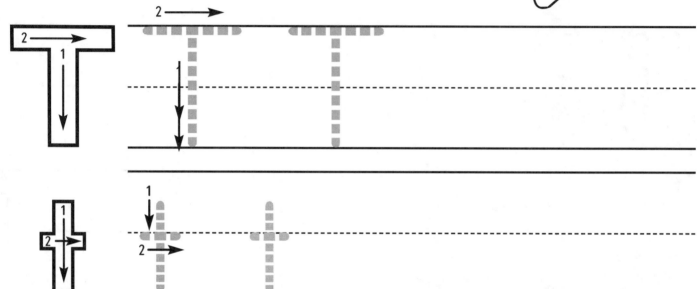

Draw a line from the table to each thing that has **T** or **t** on it.

Name_____ Date_____

Trace and write the letters.

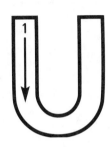
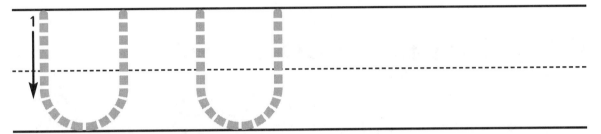

Unit 4

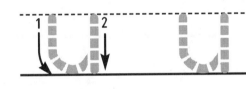

Cross out the letter on each umbrella that is not **U** or **u**.

Name_____ Date_____

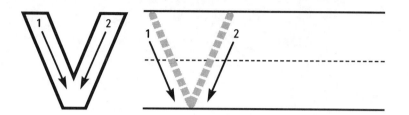
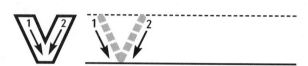

Color each valentine that has **V** or **v** on it.

Trace and write the letters.

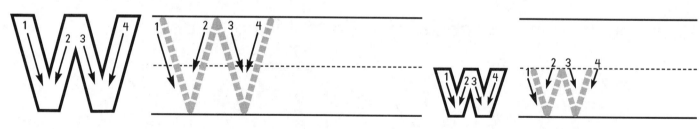

Circle each wagon that has **W** or **w** on it.

Name_____ Date_____

Trace and write the letters.

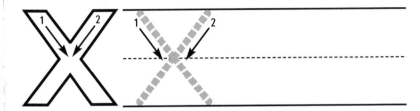 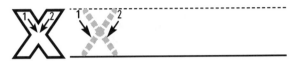

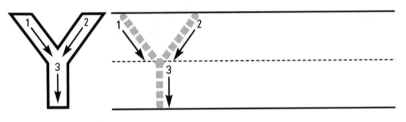 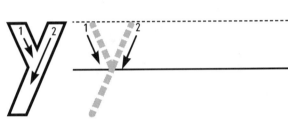

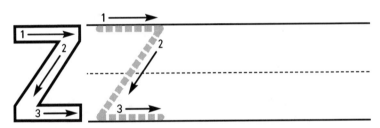 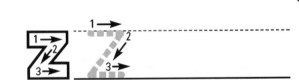

Unit 4

Draw a line from each letter to its matching partner.

 X   **y**

 Y   **z**

 **Z**   **x**

Name_____ Date_____

Connect the dots from **A** to **Z** to finish the picture.
Then color it.

Name_____ Date_____

Connect the dots from **a** to **z** to finish the picture. Then color it.

Unit 4

Name_____ Date_____

Write the missing letters.

A   B   C   _   E   F

G   H   I   J   K   _

_   M   N   O   _   Q

R   _   T   U   V

W   X   _   Z

Name_____ Date_____

Match the ones with the same beginning sound.

Unit 5

Name_____ Date_____

Circle the one with the same beginning sound as the first picture in each row.

Name_____ Date_____

Match the ones with the same beginning sound.

Unit 5

Name_____ Date_____

Color the things in the picture that have the same beginning sound as **apple**.

Name_____ Date_____

Circle the things in the picture that have the same beginning sound as **bear**.

Unit 5

Name_____ Date_____

Color the things in the picture that have the same beginning sound as **cat**.

Name_____ Date_____

Circle the things in the picture that have the same beginning sound as **dog**.

Unit 5

Name_____ Date_____

Circle the things in the picture that have the same beginning sound as **elephant**.

Name_____ Date_____

Color the footprints with things that have the same beginning sound as **fox**.

Unit 5

Name_____ Date_____

Circle the things in the picture that have the same beginning sound as **gorilla**.

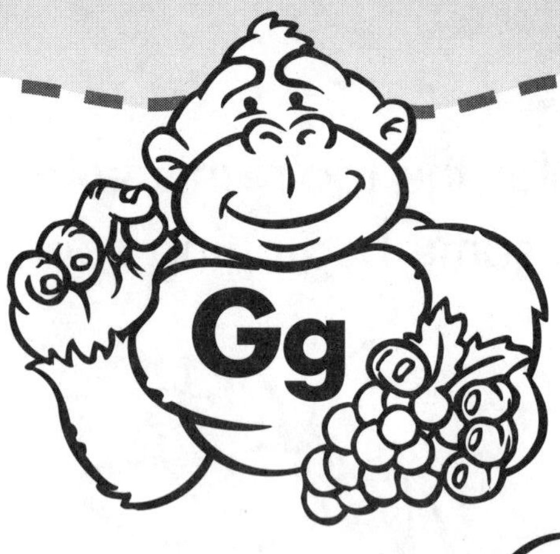

Gg

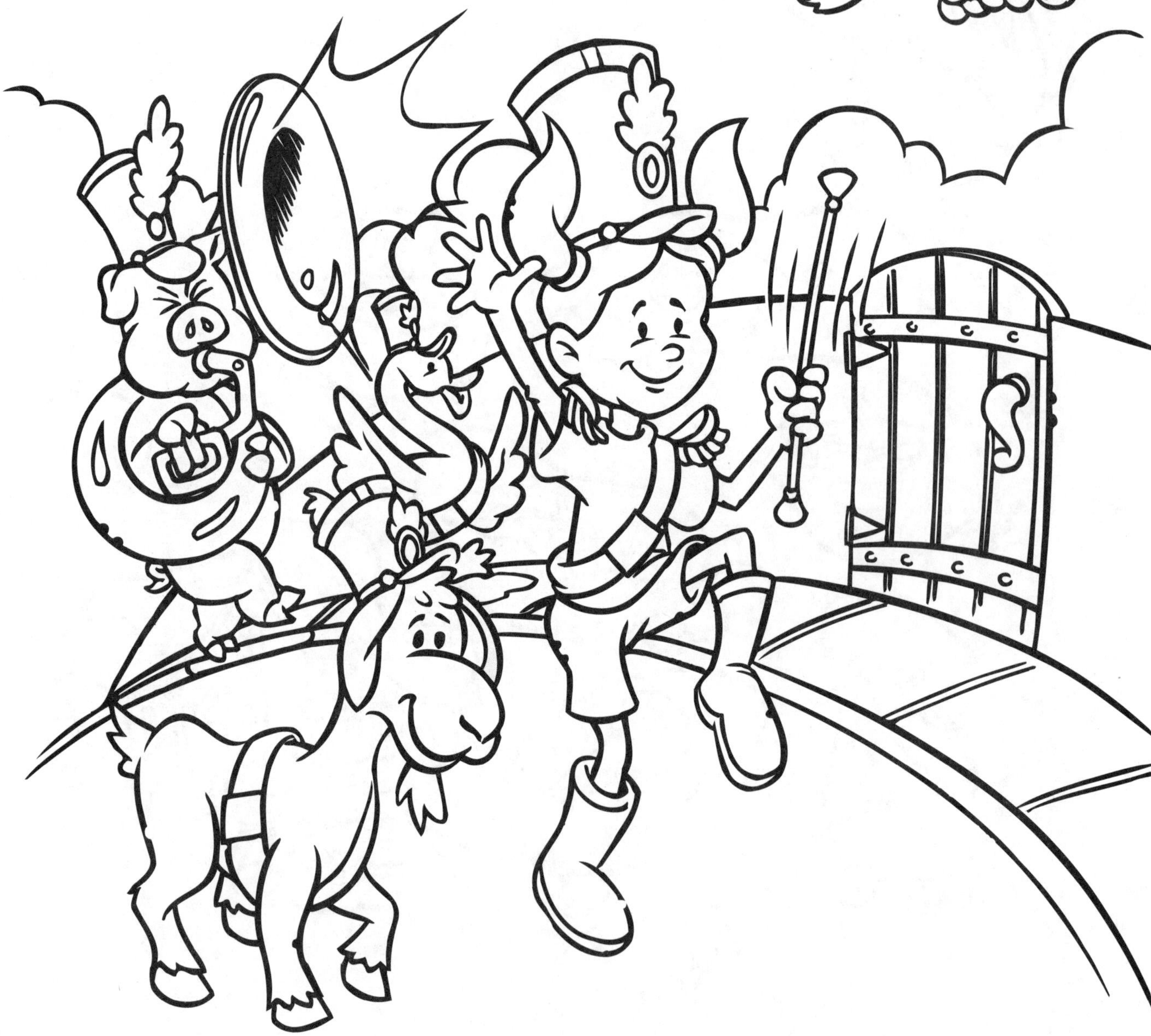

Name_____ Date_____

Color the things in the picture that have the same beginning sound as **hippo**.

Unit 5

Beginning Letter Sounds: Ii

Name_____ Date_____

Color the things in the picture that have the same beginning sound as **igloo**.

Beginning Letter Sounds: Jj

Name_____ Date_____

Circle the things in the picture that have the same beginning sound as **jack-in-the-box**.

Unit 5

Name_____ Date_____

Circle the things in the picture that have the same beginning sound as **koala**.

Name_____ Date_____

Color the things in the picture that have the same beginning sound as **lion**.

Ll

Unit 5

Name_____ Date_____

Color the things in the picture that have the same beginning sound as **monkey**.

Name_____ Date_____

Circle the things in the picture that have the same beginning sound as **nest**.

Unit 5

Name_____ Date_____

Color the things in the picture that have the same beginning sound as **octopus**.

Name_____ Date_____

Color the things in the picture that have the same beginning sound as **pig**.

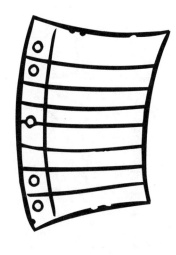

Unit 5

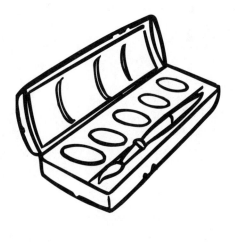

Name_____ Date_____

Circle the things in the picture that have the same beginning sound as **quail**.

Name_____ Date_____

Color the things in the picture that have the same beginning sound as **robot**.

Unit 5

Name_____ Date_____

Color the bubbles with things that have the same beginning sound as **seal**.

Name_____ Date_____

Color the spaces with things that have the same beginning sound as **turtle**.

Unit 5

Name_____ Date_____

Circle the ones that have the same beginning sound as **umpire**.

Name_____ Date_____

Color the space red if the picture has the same beginning sound as **violin**.

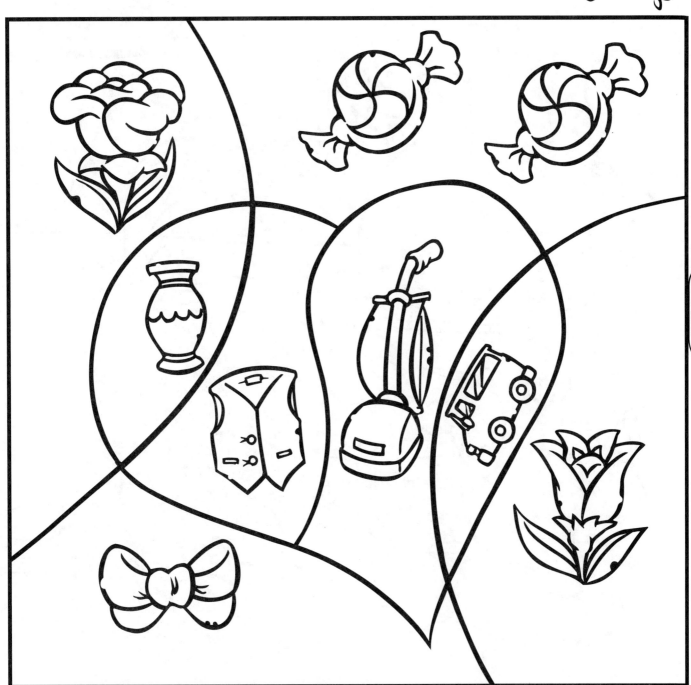

Unit 5

Name_____   Date_____

Color the things in the picture that have the same beginning sound as **weasel**.

Name_____ Date_____

Circle the ones that have the same beginning sound as **x-ray**.

Circle the ones that have the same beginning sound as **yak**.

Name_____ Date_____

Circle the things in the picture that have the same beginning sound as **zoo**.

Name_____ Date_____

Say the name of each picture. Listen to its beginning sound and then trace the letter.

Unit 5

Name_____ Date_____

Say the name of each picture. Listen to its beginning sound and then trace the letter.

Name_____ Date_____

Say the name of each picture and color it **red**. Trace the word.

red

Name_____ Date_____

Say the name of each picture and color it **yellow**.
Trace the word.

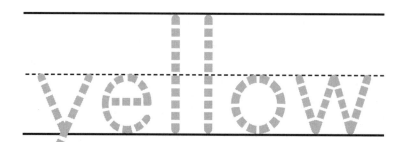

Name_____ Date_____

First color the crayons. Then color the picture.

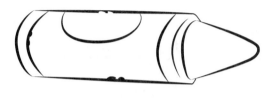

red

yellow

Unit 6

Name_____ Date_____

Say the name of each picture and color it **blue**. Trace the word.

Name_____ Date_____

Say the name of each picture and color it **green**. Trace the word.

_____

Name_____ Date_____

First color the crayons. Then color the picture.

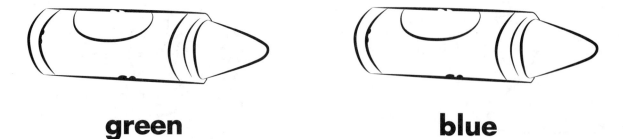

green   blue

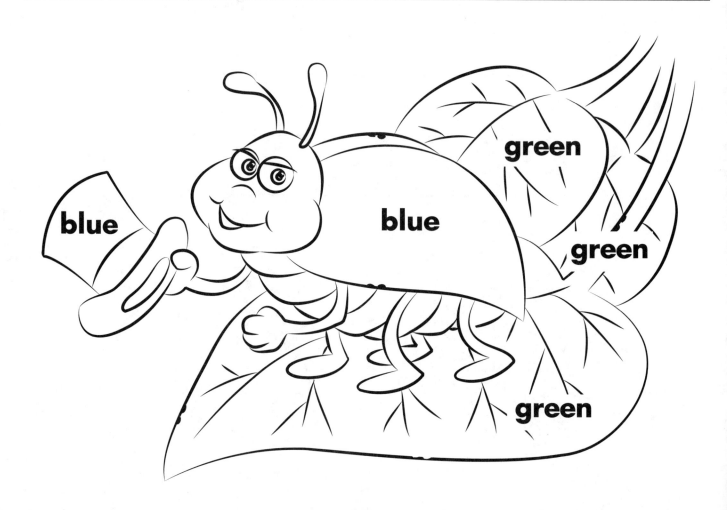

Name_____ Date_____

Say the name of each picture and color it **orange**. Trace the word.

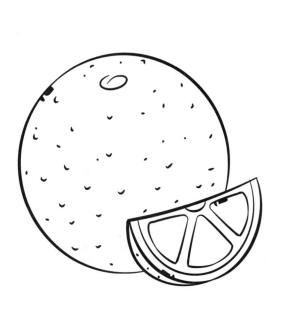 

_____

orange

Unit 6

Name_____ Date_____

Say the name of each picture and color it **black**. Trace the word.

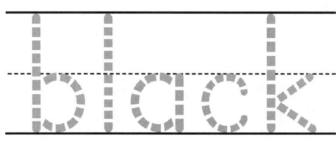

Name_____ Date_____

First color the crayons. Then color the picture.

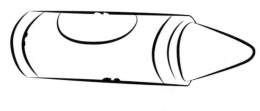

orange

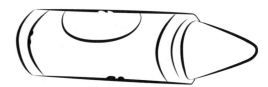

black

Unit 6

Name_____ Date_____

Say the name of each picture and color it **purple**. Trace the word.

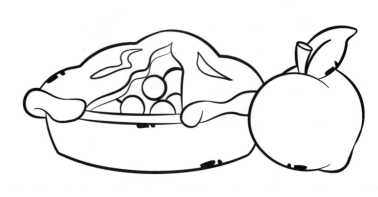

purple

Colors: Brown

Name_____ Date_____

Say the name of each picture and color it **brown**. Trace the word.

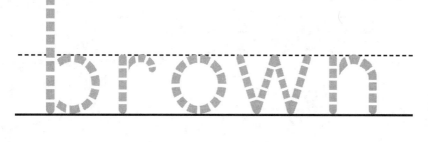

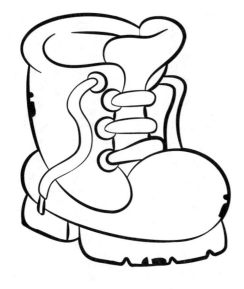 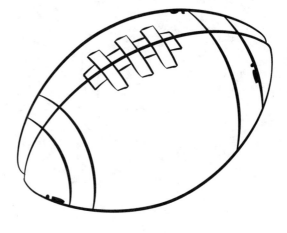

Unit 6

Name_____ Date_____

First color the crayons. Then color the picture.

purple

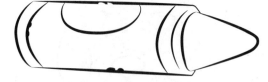

brown

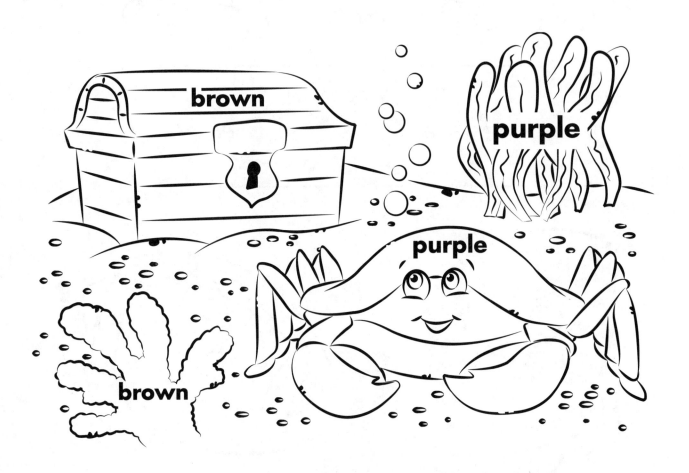

Name_____ Date_____

Look at the names for the people.

mother

father

Draw a  on father. Draw a ⌒ on mother.
Color the picture.

Unit 7

Name_____ Date_____

Look at the names for the people.

sister

brother

Draw a 🧢 on brother. Draw a 🎀 on big sister. Color the picture.

Name_____ Date_____

Look at the names for the animals.

cat

dog

Draw s on the dog. Draw ❜s on the cat.

Unit 7

Vocabulary: Names for Animals (II)

Name_____ Date_____

Look at the names for the animals.

cow   **pig**

Draw a  on the cow. Draw a ✏ on the pig. Color the picture.

Name_____ Date_____

Match the words and pictures.

dog

cow

cow

cat

pig

dog

cat

pig

Unit 7

Vocabulary: Names for Places

Name_____ Date_____

Look at the names for the places.

park   **zoo**   **beach**

Draw an **X** on the **park**.
Circle the **beach**.
Color the **zoo**.

Name_____ Date_____

Look at the names for the things.

shell   **crab**   **castle**

Draw an **X** on the **shell**.
Circle the **castle**.
Color the **crab**.

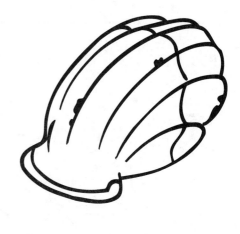

Unit 7

Opposites: Happy and Sad

Name_____ Date_____

Match the **happy** clown with its opposite.

happy

sad

Match the **sad** bunny with its opposite.

happy

sad

Name_____ Date_____

Match the **empty** nest with its opposite.

full

empty

Match the **full** toy box with its opposite.

full

empty

Unit 7

Name_____ Date_____

Look at the opposite words.

hot

cold

Draw an **X** on the **hot** snowman. Color the **cold** snowman.

Opposites: Wet and Dry

Name_____ Date_____

Look at the opposite words.

wet

dry

Draw an **X** on the **wet** bird. Color the **dry** bird.
Color the rest of the picture.

Unit 7

Opposites Review

Name_____ Date_____

Match the opposites.

dry

cold

hot

wet

sad

empty

full

happy

Name_____ Date_____

Look at the position words.

top   **bottom**

Draw an **X** on the **bottom** bricks. Color the **top** bricks.

Unit 7

Name_____ Date_____

Look at the position words.

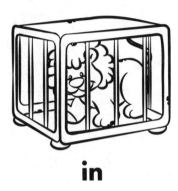

in

out

Draw an **X** on dog that is **in**. Color the dog that is **out**.

Name_____ Date_____

Match the bird that is **up** with its opposite.

up

down

Match the airplane that is **down** with its opposite.

up

down

Unit 7

Name_____ Date_____

Look at the position words.

over

under

Draw an **X** on the monkey that is **under**. Color the monkey that is **over**.

Name_____ Date_____

Match the positions to their opposites.

top

in

bottom

top

in

out

out

bottom

Unit 7

Name_____ Date_____

Color the spaces with things that rhyme.

Teaching Tip: Ask the child to name each picture on the slices of pizza. Then have him or her color the ones that rhyme. Talk about how the end of each rhyming word on the first slice has the **-op** sound. Encourage the child to give you additional words that rhyme with each group.

Name_____ Date_____

Color the pictures of things that rhyme.

Unit 7

Teaching Tip: Ask the child to name each picture on the sections of the heart. Then have him or her color the ones that rhyme. Talk about how the end of each rhyming word on the first section has the **-ie** sound. Encourage the child to give you additional words that rhyme with each group.

Picture Rhymes (III)

Name_____ Date_____

Color the pictures of things that rhyme.

Teaching Tip: Ask the child to name each picture on the plates. Then have him or her color the ones that rhyme. Talk about how the end of each rhyming word on the first plate has the **-am** sound. Encourage the child to give you additional words that rhyme with each group.

Premium Education Language Arts: Preschool   140   © Learning Horizons

Name_____ Date_____

Match the words that rhyme.

truck

plane

train

man

boat

duck

van

goat

Unit 7

Name_____ Date_____

Match the words that rhyme.

tie

ants

pants

pie

hat

two

shoe

cat

Practice Test: Self-Awareness

Name_____ Date_____

Fill in the circle next to the correct answer.

What are the people using in the pictures?

What are the people using in the pictures?

How does the bear feel in the pictures?

How does the bear feel in the pictures?

Unit 7

Name_____ Date_____

Fill in the circle next to the correct answer.

Which are the **same**? Mark them all.

Which are the **same**? Mark them all.

Which one is **different**?

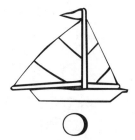  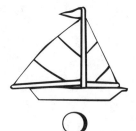 

Which one is **different**?

Name_____ Date_____

Fill in the circle next to the correct answer.

What **belongs**? Mark them all.

  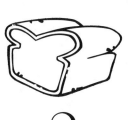 

○ ○ ○ ○

What **belongs**? Mark them all.

○ ○ ○ ○

What **does not belong**?

○ ○ ○ ○

What **does not belong**?

  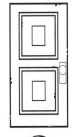 

○ ○ ○ ○

Unit 8

Name_____ Date_____

Fill in the circle next to the correct answer.

Which one correctly tells the story?

Which one comes **next**?

Name_____ Date_____

Trace the line from left to right.

Color the picture **red**.

Color the picture **yellow**.

Color the picture **blue**.

Color the picture **green**.

Color the picture **brown**.

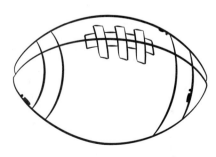

Color the picture **purple**.

Unit 8

Name_____ Date_____

Fill in the circle next to the correct answer.

Match the letters.

A	**H**	**e**	**B**	**D**
○ c	○ m	○ R	○ p	○ c
○ H	○ h	○ y	○ d	○ d
○ a	○ z	○ E	○ b	○ a

Match the letters.

f	**G**	**J**	**I**	**n**
○ d	○ T	○ e	○ i	○ N
○ S	○ c	○ U	○ L	○ S
○ F	○ g	○ j	○ o	○ u

Match the letters.

p	**Q**	**W**	**m**	**r**
○ P	○ G	○ D	○ y	○ R
○ F	○ D	○ w	○ M	○ Y
○ b	○ q	○ m	○ N	○ E

Match the letters.

T	**U**	**V**	**y**	**S**
○ P	○ c	○ W	○ T	○ c
○ t	○ H	○ u	○ v	○ s
○ Q	○ u	○ v	○ Y	○ a

Name_____ Date_____

Fill in the circle next to the correct answer.

Match the beginning sound to the letter.

○ d   ○ b   ○ s   ○ d
○ g   ○ c   ○ e   ○ a
○ u   ○ i   ○ l   ○ f

Match the beginning sound to the letter.

○ l   ○ g   ○ t   ○ m
○ a   ○ b   ○ p   ○ f
○ f   ○ p   ○ i   ○ b

Which ones rhyme with **hat** ? Mark them all.

   ○   ○   ○   ○

Which ones rhyme with **dog** ? Mark them all.

   ○   ○   ○   ○

Unit 8

Name_____ Date_____

Fill in the circle next to the correct answer.

Match the **people** with the right words.

○ mother   ○ father   ○ mother   ○ father
○ sister   ○ brother   ○ sister   ○ brother

Match the **animals** with the right word.

○ pig   ○ cat   ○ pig   ○ cat
○ cow   ○ cow   ○ dog   ○ dog

Which ones show the opposite of **empty**? Mark them all.

○   ○   ○   ○

Which ones show the opposite of **down**? Mark them all.

○   ○   ○   ○

Answer Key

Page 3

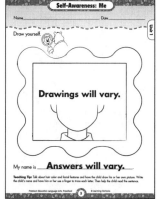

Page 4

Page 5

Page 6

Page 7

Page 8

Page 9

Page 10

Answer Key

Page 11

Page 12

Page 13

Page 14
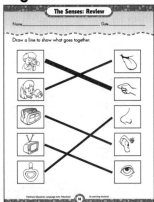

Page 15

Page 16

Page 17

Page 18

Page 19

Page 20

Page 21

Page 22

Page 23

Page 24

Page 25

Page 26

Answer Key

Page 27

Page 28

Page 29

Page 30

Page 31

Page 32

Page 33

Page 34

Page 35

Page 36

Page 37

Page 38

Page 39

Page 40
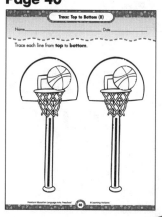

Page 41
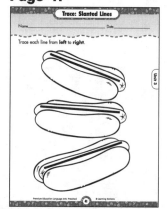

Page 42
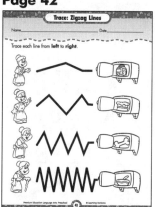

Answers

Answer Key

Page 43

Page 44
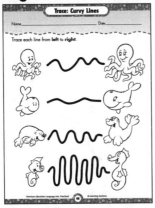

Page 45

Page 46

Page 47

Page 48

Page 49

Page 50

Page 51

Page 52

Page 53

Page 54

Page 55

Page 56

Page 57

Page 58

Answer Key

Page 59
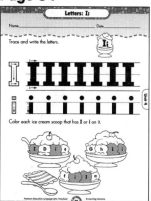

Page 60

Page 61

Page 62

Page 63

Page 64
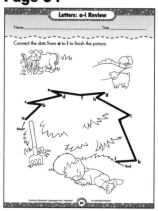

Page 65

Page 66

Page 67

Page 68
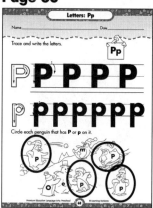

Page 69

Page 70

Page 71

Page 72
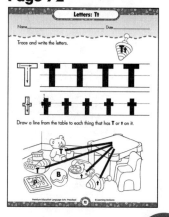

Page 73

Page 74
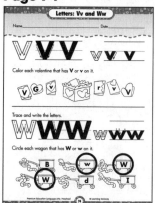

Answer Key

Page 75
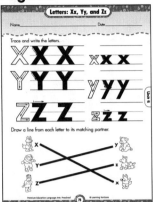

Page 76

Page 77

Page 78

Page 79

Page 80

Page 81

Page 82

Page 83

Page 84

Page 85

Page 86

Page 87

Page 88
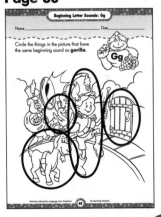

Page 89

Page 90

Answer Key

Page 91

Page 92

Page 93

Page 94

Page 95

Page 96

Page 97

Page 98

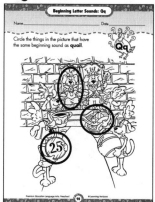

Page 99

Page 100

Page 101

Page 102

Page 103

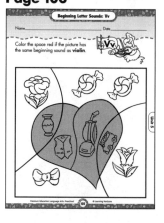

Page 104

Page 105

Page 106

Answer Key

Page 107

Page 108

Page 109
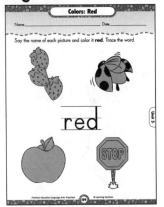

Page 110

Page 111
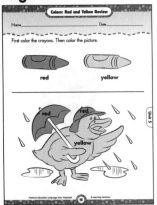

Page 112

Page 113

Page 114
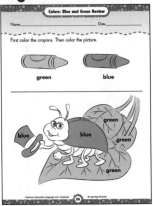

Page 115

Page 116
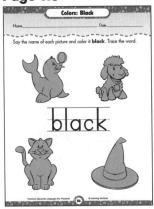

Page 117

Page 118
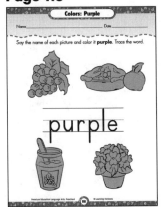

Page 119

Page 120

Page 121

Page 122

Answer Key

Page 123

Page 124

Page 125

Page 126

Page 127

Page 128

Page 129

Page 130

Page 131

Page 132
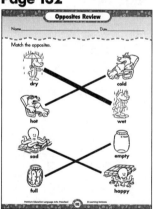

Page 133

Page 134

Page 135

Page 136
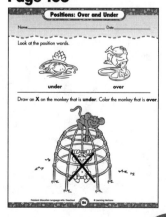

Page 137
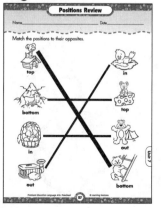

Page 138

Answer Key

Page 139

Picture Rhymes (II) — Color the pictures of things that rhyme.

Page 140

Picture Rhymes (III) — Color the pictures of things that rhyme.

Page 141

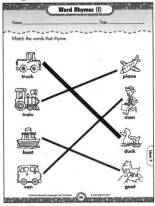

Word Rhymes (I) — Match the words that rhyme.

Page 142

Word Rhymes (II) — Match the words that rhyme.

Page 143

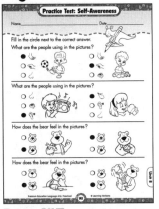

Practice Test: Self-Awareness

Page 144

Practice Test: Visual Discrimination

Page 145

Practice Test: Classifying

Page 146

Practice Test: Sequence and Predictions

Page 147

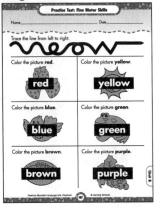

Practice Test: Fine Motor Skills

Page 148

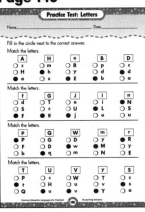

Practice Test: Letters

Page 149

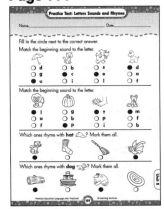

Practice Test: Letters Sounds and Rhymes

Page 150

Practice Test: Vocabulary and Opposites